POPULAR
MUSIC THEORY

Workbook

GRADE 5

www.rockschool.co.uk

Acknowledgements

Published by Rockschool Ltd. © 2015
Catalogue Number RSK011508
ISBN: 978-1-908920-74-4

Publishing
Written, compiled and edited by Simon Troup, Jennie Troup and Stuart Slater.
Internal design and layout by Simon and Jennie Troup, Digital Music Art.
Cover designed by Philip Millard, Philip Millard Design.
Additional proofing by Chris Bird, Owen Bailey, Nik Preston, Mike Stylianou, Joanna Taman and Mary Keene.

Syllabus Consultants
Rachael Meech, Mike Stylianou, Joanna Taman and Anna Cook.

Contributors
Prof. Joe Bennett, Simon Niblock, Jonathan Preiss, Stefan Redtenbacher, Philip Henderson and Martin Hibbert.

Images & Illustrations
p. 26 | © iStock.com/craftvision
pp. 27 & 50 | © Dean Bertoncelj / Shutterstock.com

Printing
Printed and bound in the United Kingdom by Caligraving Ltd.

Distribution
Exclusive Distributors: Music Sales Ltd.

Contacting Rockschool
www.rockschool.co.uk
Telephone: +44 (0)845 460 4747
Email: info@rockschool.co.uk

Table of Contents

Introductions & Information

Page

Theory Exam Sections

Page

Sample Paper

Page

Additional Information

Page

Welcome to Rockschool Popular Music Theory – Grade 5

Rockschool publish two sets of books to help candidates prepare for theory examinations – the *Rockschool Popular Music Theory Guidebooks* and *Rockschool Popular Music Theory Workbooks.*

The guidebooks are a teaching resource for candidates to work through the material required for the Rockschool theory syllabus with the support of their teacher.

To complement the guidebooks, a set of workbooks provide a series of exercises and sample papers in which to practise the skills introduced in the guidebooks.

Entering Rockschool Examinations

It's now easier than ever to enter a Rockschool examination. Simply go to *www.rockschool.co.uk/enter-online* to book your exam online today.

Syllabus Content Overview

An overview of the syllabus content covered at this grade can be found at the back of this book. As this is a cumulative syllabus, you can download overviews for all grades from the Rockschool website at *www.rockschool.co.uk/theory* along with other theory syllabus related resources.

Exam Format

The exam has four sections. These are:

- **Music Notation** (20%)
  In this section, all questions relate to music notation.

- **Popular Music Harmony** (25%)
  In this section, all questions relate to music harmony.

- **Band Knowledge** (25%)
  This section is in two parts, with each part covering a range of instruments:
  - **Part 1:** Identification
  - **Part 2:** Notation and Techniques

- **Band Analysis** (30%)
  In this section, the questions will include the identification of music notation, harmony and the stylistic characteristics of drums, guitar, bass, keys and vocals in a multi-instrumental context.

SECTION 1 | MUSIC NOTATION

SUMMARY	
SECTION *(Current section highlighted)*	**MARKS**
> **Music Notation**	**20 [20%]**
Popular Music Harmony	25 [25%]
Band Knowledge	25 [25%]
Band Analysis	30 [30%]

The *Music Notation* section of Rockschool Theory Examinations covers the following:

- 1.1 Pitch
- 1.2 Note length/rhythm
- 1.3 Dynamics, articulations and phrasing

You will be presented with a variety of exercises to hone your understanding and skills in these areas within the content specified for this grade.

Content Overview

An overview of the syllabus content covered at this grade can be found at the back of this book. As this is a cumulative syllabus, you can download overviews for all grades from the Rockschool website at *www.rockschool.co.uk*.

Section 1 | Music Notation

Rhythm | Halving and doubling rhythmic values

1. Rewrite this phrase to fit the same number of bars in the new time signature, adjusting the rhythmic values as necessary:

2. Rewrite this phrase to fit the same number of bars in the new time signature, adjusting the rhythmic values as necessary:

3. Rewrite this phrase to fit the same number of bars in the new time signature, adjusting the rhythmic values as necessary:

4. Rewrite this phrase to fit the same number of bars in the new time signature, adjusting the rhythmic values as necessary:

Rhythm | $\frac{6}{8}$ and $\frac{12}{8}$

1. Rewrite this phrase to fit the same number of bars in the new time signature, adjusting the rhythmic values as necessary:

2. Rewrite this phrase to fit the same number of bars in the new time signature, adjusting the rhythmic values as necessary:

3. Rewrite this phrase to fit the same number of bars in the new time signature, adjusting the rhythmic values as necessary:

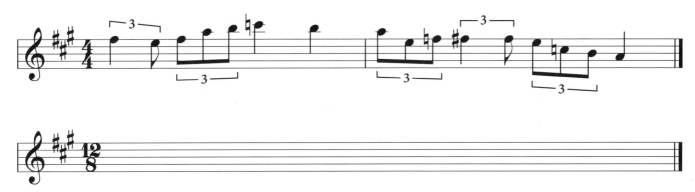

4. Rewrite this phrase to fit the same number of bars in the new time signature, adjusting the rhythmic values as necessary:

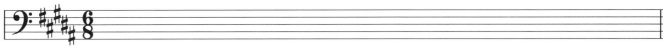

Section 1 | Music Notation

Pitch | Ledger lines

1. Copy the notes from the stave on the left to the stave on the right. Maintain the same pitch without the use of octave notation:

2. Copy the notes from the stave on the left to the stave on the right. Maintain the same pitch without the use of octave notation:

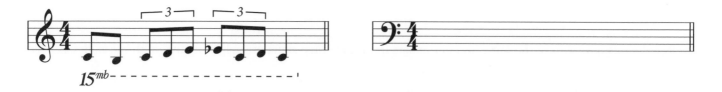

3. Copy the notes from the stave on the left to the stave on the right. *Use octave notation* and maintain the same pitch:

4. Copy the notes from the stave on the left to the stave on the right. *Use octave notation* and maintain the same pitch:

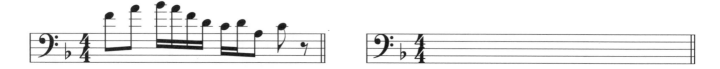

5. Copy the notes from the stave on the left to the stave on the right. *Use octave notation* and maintain the same pitch. Use accidentals instead of a key signature:

6. Copy the notes from the stave on the left to the stave on the right. *Use octave notation* and maintain the same pitch. Use accidentals instead of a key signature:

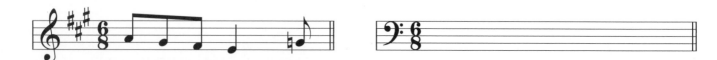

Pitch | Ledger lines

1. Copy bar 1 of the upper stave into bar 2 of the lower stave, two octaves lower, maintaining the use of bass clef:

What is name of the highest note played in the treble clef? ....

What is name of the lowest note played in the bass clef (after copying the notes)? ....

How many octaves apart are the highest and lowest notes in the example (after copying the notes)? ....

2. Copy bar 1 of the upper stave into bar 1 of the lower stave, two octaves lower, maintaining the use of bass clef:

What is name of the highest note played in the treble clef? ....

What is name of the lowest note played in the bass clef (after copying the notes)? ....

How many octaves apart are the highest and lowest notes in the example (after copying the notes)? ....

Section 1 | Music Notation

Dynamics & Articulations

The following ten questions refer to the six-bar extract of bass-guitar notation below:

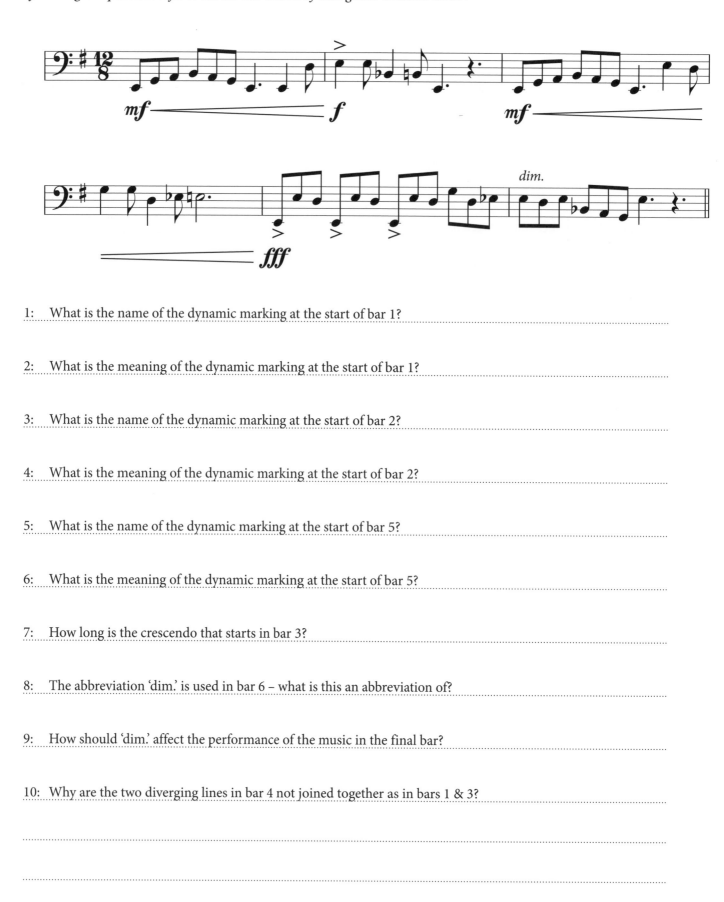

1:   What is the name of the dynamic marking at the start of bar 1?

2:   What is the meaning of the dynamic marking at the start of bar 1?

3:   What is the name of the dynamic marking at the start of bar 2?

4:   What is the meaning of the dynamic marking at the start of bar 2?

5:   What is the name of the dynamic marking at the start of bar 5?

6:   What is the meaning of the dynamic marking at the start of bar 5?

7:   How long is the crescendo that starts in bar 3?

8:   The abbreviation 'dim.' is used in bar 6 – what is this an abbreviation of?

9:   How should 'dim.' affect the performance of the music in the final bar?

10: Why are the two diverging lines in bar 4 not joined together as in bars 1 & 3?

Dynamics & Articulations

The following ten tasks require you to add notation to the six-bar extract of bass-guitar notation below:

1: Indicate that beats 1 to 3 of bar 1 should be played legato.

2: Indicate that the piece starts quietly.

3: Indicate that the piece builds in volume from quiet in bar 1 beat 1, to loud in bar 2 beat 1.

4: Add the dynamic marking pianissimo to beat 1 of bar 3.

5: Indicate that the last note of bar 4 is played extremely loudly.

6: Add a crescendo between the dynamic markings you created in steps 4 & 5.

7: Indicate that a trill should be played on the last note of bar 4.

8: Add accents to the three low E notes in bar 5.

9: Add staccatos to the eighth notes in bar 6.

10: Add a fermata to the last note.

Section 1 | Music Notation

Dynamics & Articulations

The following two tasks refer to the four-bar extract of piano music below:

1. Name and briefly define the articulations that appear in the musical extract:

    ....

    ....

    ....

    ....

    ....

    ....

    ....

2. Complete the chart below, then add one of each of the dyamic markings from the chart into the score above. Use the existing notation, dynamics and articulations as an aid to placing the dynamics in a meaningful place:

SYMBOL	MUSICAL TERM	MEANING
fp		Loudly then immediately softly
sfp		
ppp	Pianississimo	
fff		

SECTION 2 | POPULAR MUSIC HARMONY

SUMMARY	
SECTION (*Current section highlighted*)	**MARKS**
Music Notation	20 [20%]
> **Popular Music Harmony**	**25 [25%]**
Band Knowledge	25 [25%]
Band Analysis	30 [30%]

The *Popular Music Harmony* section of Rockschool Theory Examinations covers the following:

- 2.1   Scales and related intervals
- 2.2   Chords

You will be presented with a variety of exercises to hone your understanding and skills in these areas within the content specified for this grade.

Content Overview

An overview of the syllabus content covered at this grade can be found at the back of this book. As this is a cumulative syllabus, you can download overviews for all grades from the Rockschool website at *www.rockschool.co.uk*.

Section 2 | Popular Music Harmony

Intervals | Identifying intervals

1. Identify the following melodic intervals by ticking the correct box below each example:

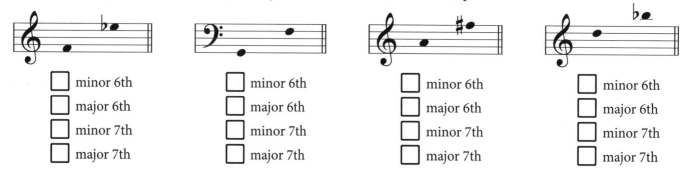

☐ minor 6th	☐ minor 6th	☐ minor 6th	☐ minor 6th
☐ major 6th	☐ major 6th	☐ major 6th	☐ major 6th
☐ minor 7th	☐ minor 7th	☐ minor 7th	☐ minor 7th
☐ major 7th	☐ major 7th	☐ major 7th	☐ major 7th

2. Identify the following melodic intervals by writing their names on the line below each example:

....

3. Identify the following harmonic intervals by writing their names on the line below each example:

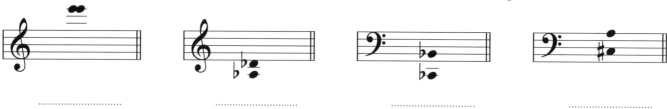

....

4. Identify the following harmonic intervals by writing their names on the line below each example:

....

5. Identify the following melodic intervals by writing their names on the line below each example:

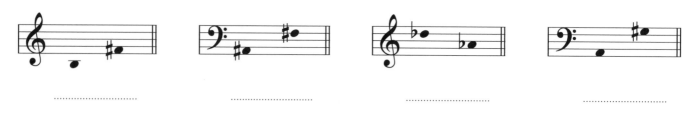

....

6. Identify the following melodic intervals by writing their names on the line below each example:

....

Scales | Scale identification

1. Examine the following scale then answer the two questions below:

Name the scale:

How does this scale differ from the natural minor?

2. Name the scales used by the following riffs. Write your answer below each example:

3. Name the scales used by the following riffs. Write your answer below each example:

4. Name the scales used by the following riffs. Write your answer below each example:

Section 2 | Popular Music Harmony

Scales | Applying scale knowledge

1. One or more accidentals are missing from this B harmonic minor scale. Underline any wrong notes and add their accidentals:

   B   C♯   D   E   F   G   A   B

2. Put circles around any notes that are **not** in the B♭ blues scale:

   C♮   D♯   E♭   F   G♯   A♮   B♭   C♯   D♮   E   F♯   G♮   A♭

3. Write out the letter names (with their accidentals if appropriate) of the B major scale:

   Your answer: ....

4. One or more accidentals are missing from this D♭ major scale. Underline any wrong notes and add their accidentals:

   D♭   E   F   G   A   B   C   D♭

5. One or more accidentals are missing from this G♯ natural minor scale. Underline any wrong notes and add their accidentals:

   G♯   A   B   C   D   E   F   G♯

6. Look at each note in turn, circling those that can be found in the D♭ blues scale:

   B♭   G♮   E   D   C♯   F   A   D♭   A♮   G   E♮   F♯   B   C

7. Name two different scale *types* where the seventh degree of the scale is a major 7th interval above the root:

   Your answer: ....

Scales | Adding accidentals

1. Add the missing accidentals to the scale below:

Db major

2. Add the missing accidentals to the scale below:

F harmonic minor

3. Add the missing accidentals to the scale below:

F# minor pentatonic

4. Add the missing accidentals to the scale below:

B blues

5. Add the missing accidentals to the scale below:

B harmonic minor

6. Add the missing accidentals to the scale below:

A major pentatonic

Section 2 | Popular Music Harmony

Scales | Writing scales

1. Using the *treble* clef and correct key signature, write a one-octave *descending* scale of G harmonic minor in whole notes:

   G harmonic minor

2. Using the *bass* clef and correct key signature, write a one-octave *descending* scale of C♯ minor pentatonic in whole notes:

   C♯ minor pentatonic

3. Using the *bass* clef and correct key signature, write a one-octave *ascending* scale of B major pentatonic in whole notes:

   B major pentatonic

4. Using the *treble* clef and correct key signature, write a one-octave *ascending* scale of A major pentatonic in whole notes:

   A major pentatonic

5. Using the *treble* clef and correct key signature, write a one-octave *descending* scale of F♯ harmonic minor in whole notes:

   F♯ harmonic minor

6. Using the *treble* clef and correct key signature, write a one-octave *ascending* B♭ blues scale in whole notes:

   B♭ blues

Scales | Writing accidentals

1. Add the key signature to the top stave to fit the named scale, then write out the example again using accidentals instead of a key signature:

D natural minor

2. Add the key signature to the top stave to fit the named scale, then write out the example again using accidentals instead of a key signature:

B major

3. Add the key signature to the top stave to fit the named scale, then write out the example again using accidentals instead of a key signature:

G♯ minor pentatonic

Section 2 | Popular Music Harmony

Scales | Writing accidentals

1. Identify the scale by writing its name on the line provided below, then rewrite the example using the correct key signature, adding accidentals only as required:

Scale name: ....

2. Identify the scale by writing its name on the line provided below, then rewrite the example using the correct key signature, adding accidentals only as required:

Scale name: ....

3. Identify the scale by writing its name on the line provided below, then rewrite the example using the correct key signature, adding accidentals only as required:

Scale name: ....

Chords | Naming and inversions

1. Write the chord names below the following chords:

....

2. Write the chord names and their inversions below the following chords:

.... G major ....

.... 1st inversion ....

3. Write the chord names and their inversions below the following chords:

....

....

4. Add chords to the empty staves as directed by the text below the stave:

G minor   E minor   D♭ major   A♭ major

2nd inversion   1st inversion   1st inversion   2nd inversion

5. Add chords to the empty staves as directed by the text below the stave:

C/E   C♯m/E   B♭m/F   E/G♯

Section 2 | Popular Music Harmony

Chords | Transposing Roman numeral charts

1a.   Write the chord names above the chord chart assuming a key of D major:

$$\left\|\begin{matrix}\textbf{4}\\\textbf{4}\end{matrix}\right.\quad \text{I} \quad / \quad / \quad / \quad \bigg| \quad \text{IV} \quad / \quad \text{IVm} \quad / \quad \bigg| \quad \text{VIm} \quad / \quad \text{V}^7 \quad / \quad \bigg| \quad \text{I} \quad / \quad / \quad / \quad \right\|$$

1b.   Here is the same chord chart again – repeat the exercise but this time assume a key of F major:

$$\left\|\begin{matrix}\textbf{4}\\\textbf{4}\end{matrix}\right.\quad \text{I} \quad / \quad / \quad / \quad \bigg| \quad \text{IV} \quad / \quad \text{IVm} \quad / \quad \bigg| \quad \text{VIm} \quad / \quad \text{V}^7 \quad / \quad \bigg| \quad \text{I} \quad / \quad / \quad / \quad \right\|$$

2a.   Write the chord names above the chord chart assuming a key of B♭ major:

$$\left\|\begin{matrix}\textbf{4}\\\textbf{4}\end{matrix}\right.\quad \text{Imaj}^7 \quad / \quad \text{VI}^7 \quad / \quad \bigg| \quad \text{IIm}^7 \quad / \quad \text{V}^7 \quad / \quad \bigg| \quad \text{IIIm}^7 \quad / \quad \text{VI}^7 \quad / \quad \bigg| \quad \text{IIm}^7 \quad \text{♭II}^7 \quad \text{Imaj}^7 \quad / \quad \right\|$$

2b.   Here is the same chord chart again – repeat the exercise but this time assume a key of C major:

$$\left\|\begin{matrix}\textbf{4}\\\textbf{4}\end{matrix}\right.\quad \text{Imaj}^7 \quad / \quad \text{VI}^7 \quad / \quad \bigg| \quad \text{IIm}^7 \quad / \quad \text{V}^7 \quad / \quad \bigg| \quad \text{IIIm}^7 \quad / \quad \text{VI}^7 \quad / \quad \bigg| \quad \text{IIm}^7 \quad \text{♭II}^7 \quad \text{Imaj}^7 \quad / \quad \right\|$$

3a.   Write the chord names above the chord chart assuming a key of A minor:

$$\left\|\begin{matrix}\textbf{4}\\\textbf{4}\end{matrix}\right.\quad \text{Im} \quad / \quad \text{VII} \quad / \quad \bigg| \quad \text{IV} \quad / \quad \text{VI} \quad / \quad \bigg| \quad \text{Im} \quad / \quad \text{V}^7 \quad / \quad \bigg| \quad \text{Im} \quad / \quad / \quad / \quad \right\|$$

3b.   Here is the same chord chart again – repeat the exercise but this time assume a key of F minor:

$$\left\|\begin{matrix}\textbf{4}\\\textbf{4}\end{matrix}\right.\quad \text{Im} \quad / \quad \text{VII} \quad / \quad \bigg| \quad \text{IV} \quad / \quad \text{VI} \quad / \quad \bigg| \quad \text{Im} \quad / \quad \text{V}^7 \quad / \quad \bigg| \quad \text{Im} \quad / \quad / \quad / \quad \right\|$$

Chords | Applying chord knowledge

1a. Add Roman numerals for the following chord sequence onto the dotted line provided below the stave:

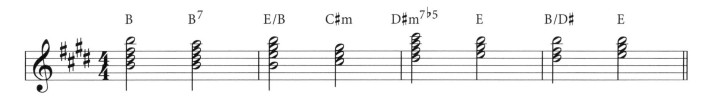

....

1b. Transpose the chord sequence above into the key of A major, adding the appropriate key signature and new chord symbols above the stave:

2a. Add Roman numerals for the following chord sequence onto the dotted line provided below the stave:

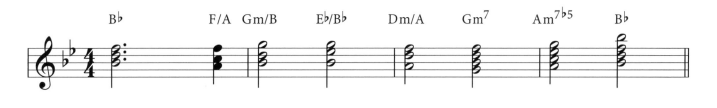

....

2b. Transpose the chord sequence above into the key of B major, adding the appropriate key signature and new chord symbols above the stave:

Section 2 | Popular Music Harmony

Chords | Applying chord knowledge

1. Circle the notes found in a B major^7 chord:

       B   C   C♯   D   D♯   E   F   F♯   G   G♯   A   A♯   B

2. Circle the notes found in a C minor$^{7♭5}$ chord:

       C   D♭   D   E♭   E   F   G♭   G   A♭   A   B♭   B   C

3. Write out the letter names (with their accidentals if appropriate) of a G♯ minor^7 chord:

   Your answer: ....

4. Add one or more accidentals to the following notes to create an F minor^7 chord:

       F   A   C   E

5. Add one or more accidentals to the following notes to create a B♭ major^7 chord:

       B   D   F   A

6. Look at each note in turn, circling those that can be found in a C♯ minor$^{7♭5}$ chord:

       B♭   G♮   E   D   C♯   F   A   D♭   A♮   G   E♮   F♯   B   C

7. Write out the note names in a 2nd inversion F♯ minor chord (low to high):

   Your answer: ....

Section 3 | Band Knowledge

SUMMARY	
SECTION *(Current section highlighted)*	**MARKS**
Music Notation	20 [20%]
Popular Music Harmony	25 [25%]
> **Band Knowledge**	**25 [25%]**
Band Analysis	30 [30%]

The *Band Knowledge* section of Rockschool Theory Examinations covers the following:

- 3.1   Identify instrument parts and function
- 3.2   Identify instrument-specific notation
- 3.3   Identify instrumental techniques

You will be presented with a variety of exercises to hone your understanding and skills in these areas within the content specified for this grade.

Content Overview

An overview of the syllabus content covered at this grade can be found at the back of this book. As this is a cumulative syllabus, you can download overviews for all grades from the Rockschool website at *www.rockschool.co.uk*.

Section 3 | Band Knowledge

Part 1 | Identification | Drums

The following task requires you to identify parts of the hi-hat as labelled in the image on the right:

1. Name each of the labelled parts in the image:

    A) ....

    B) ....

    C) ....

    D) ....

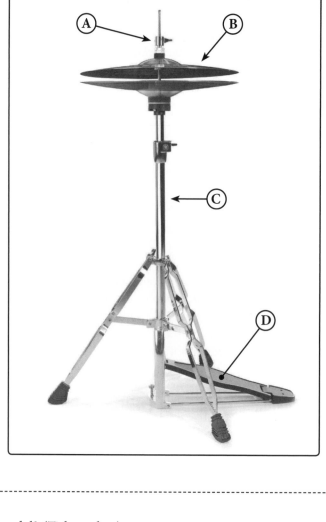

----

2. Which style of music is most likely to use a double bass-drum pedal? *(Tick one box)*

    ☐ Soul   ☐ Jazz   ☐ Metal   ☐ Pop

3. A double bass pedal has two footplates. The first is placed directly in front of the bass drum. Where is the other placed?

    Your answer: ....

True or false:

4. Drum brushes sometimes have retractable heads: ☐ True   ☐ False

5. Drum brushes are typically used in blues and jazz: ☐ True   ☐ False

6. A tuning key is found on all cymbal stands: ☐ True   ☐ False

7. The ride cymbal is also called the crash cymbal: ☐ True   ☐ False

8. Toms are types of small cymbals: ☐ True   ☐ False

Part 1 | Identification | Guitar and Bass

The following task requires you to identify parts of the guitar as labelled in the picture on the right:

1. Name each of the labelled parts in the image:

A) ....

B) ....

C) ....

D) ....

E) ....

F) ....

---

2. Into which socket on an amplifier would you plug in a guitar cable? *(Tick one box)*

☐ Input   ☐ Speaker output   ☐ Effects send   ☐ Headphone socket

3. Which control changes the level of the signal sent from the guitar to the amplifier? *(Tick one box)*

☐ Foot switch   ☐ Tone control   ☐ Pickup selector   ☐ Volume control

4. How many tuning pegs would you expect to find on a standard electric guitar? *(Tick one box)*

☐ 4   ☐ 5   ☐ 6   ☐ 7

---

5. Below is a description of a jack socket. Complete the sentence by filling in the blank spaces with the correct terms:

A .... is plugged into the jack socket and carries the .... from the

.... to the .... which amplifies the signal.

Section 3 | Band Knowledge

Part 1 | Identification | Keys

Match the correct description with the three different standard EQ settings: *(Tick one box per question)*

1. This control makes the sound fuller and warmer: ☐ Treble ☐ Middle ☐ Bass

2. This makes the sound light and sparkly: ☐ Treble ☐ Middle ☐ Bass

3. This is the setting between the high and low setting: ☐ Treble ☐ Middle ☐ Bass

----

True or false:

4. There are no EQ controls on an acoustic piano: ☐ True ☐ False

5. EQ in music audio means 'equal quality': ☐ True ☐ False

6. EQ on an electronic keyboard changes the volume of a patch: ☐ True ☐ False

7. EQ on an electronic keyboard changes the sound quality of a patch: ☐ True ☐ False

8. There are four settings in a standard (basic) EQ section: ☐ True ☐ False

----

Fill in the blanks:

9. The .... supplies power to an electronic keyboard. The .... for the adaptor can be found on the panel at the back of the keyboard.

10: The .... pedal lifts the damper off the strings on an .... piano which allows the sound to ring out.

11: The .... pedal is on the left at the bottom of an acoustic piano. This pedal affects the sound by shifting the keyboard to the right. This means the .... can only hit one or two of the three strings and so reduces the volume.

12: An .... piano creates sound without the need for a power source. When a key is pressed it causes a hammer to strike a .... creating the familiar piano sound.

Part 1 | Identification | Vocals

1. Which part of a microphone is designed to vibrate when it picks up sound? *(Tick one box)*

   ☐ Soft palate   ☐ Diaphragm   ☐ Pickup coil   ☐ Larynx

---

2. Which is the correct description of how a microphone works? *(Tick one box)*

   ☐ The electrical signals picked up by a microphone are converted into vibrations and sent to the PA via a jack socket.

   ☐ The vibrations picked up by the PA are turned into an electrical signal which is sent to the microphone via a cable.

   ☐ The vibrations picked up by a microphone are converted into an electrical signal which is sent via a cable to the PA.

What are the four basic controls found on a PA? Give a brief description of how each of these controls affects the sound:

3. ....

   ....

4. ....

   ....

5. ....

   ....

6. ....

   ....

Fill in the blanks:

7. PA stands for .... PA systems can handle more than one input at a time. The number of microphones

   and/or instruments they can amplify is determined by the number of separate .... provided.

Section 3 | Band Knowledge

Part 2 | Notation & Techniques | Drums

The following four questions refer to the one-bar of drum notation on the right:

Each beat of the bar uses a different snare-drum technique. Identify the technique and then give a brief description of how a drummer would create this sound:

1a.   Beat 1 | Name of technique: ....

1b.   Beat 1 | Description: ....

2a.   Beat 2 | Name of technique: ....

2b.   Beat 2 | Description: ....

3a.   Beat 3 | Name of technique: ....

3b.   Beat 3 | Description: ....

4a.   Beat 4 | Name of technique: ....

4b.   Beat 4 | Description: ....

----

5.   In which style of music are you most likely to find hi-hat stepping? *(Tick one box)*

☐ Heavy metal   ☐ Hip hop   ☐ Jazz   ☐ Pop

6.   Describe how a drummer would play the hi-hat to create a hi-hat stepping pattern:

Your answer: ....

....

....

....

....

Part 2 | Notation & Techniques | Guitar and Bass

The following two questions refer to the one-bar extract of notation on the right:

1. Which note is the lowest note that a standard guitar can play? *(Tick one box)*

   ☐ 1   ☐ 2   ☐ 3   ☐ 4   ☐ 5

2. Which note is the lowest note that a standard bass guitar can play? *(Tick one box)*

   ☐ 1   ☐ 2   ☐ 3   ☐ 4   ☐ 5

- -

The following five questions refer to the two-bar extract of guitar notation below:

3. What is the wavy line over the final note of bar 1 called? ....

4. How would this note be played to create this effect? ....

5. What does the *8va* symbol in bar 2 mean? ....

6. What kind of harmonics are used in the second bar? *(Tick one box)*

   ☐ Neutral   ☐ Neural   ☐ Natural   ☐ Ninth

7. Briefly explain how a guitarist would play the harmonics in bar 2:

   Your answer: ....

   ....

   ....

Section 3 | Band Knowledge

Part 2 | Notation & Techniques | Keyboards

The following five tasks require you to add notation to the two-bar piano music extract below:

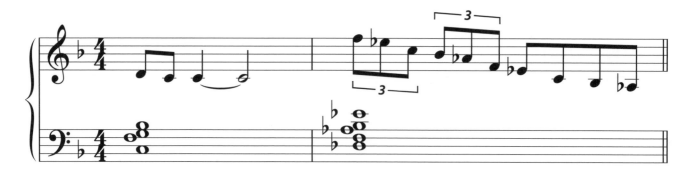

On the right-hand part:
1. Place a trill symbol on the second, third and fourth beats of bar 1.
2. Place a glissando symbol between the final note of the first bar up to the first note of bar 2.
3. Place staccato indications on the final four eighth notes of the extract.

On the left-hand part:
4. Place a tenuto symbol on the chord in bar 1.
5. Place an accent on the chord in bar 2.

---

6. What does the term *trill* tell the player to do? *(Tick one box)*

   ☐ Bend the note with a pitch modulator.

   ☐ Rapidly alternate between the written note and the tone or semitone above.

   ☐ Play the note several times in rapid succession.

   ☐ Rapidly alter the volume up and down.

How would a keyboardist play a note with a tenuto symbol differently to a note with an accent symbol?

   Your answer: ....

   ....

Describe how a keyboardist would play a staccato note:

   Your answer: ....

   ....

Part 2 | Notation & Techniques | Vocals

The following two questions refer to the two-bar extract of vocal music below:

1. Describe how the singer would sing the final note of bar 1 and the first beat of bar 2:

   Your answer: ....

   ....

2. Name and describe the function of the horizontal line to the right of the lyrics "oa" on the final note of bar 1 and the first beat of bar 2:

   Your answer: ....

   ....

- -

True or false:

3. Vocal vibrato is a subtle oscillation in the pitch of a note: ☐ True ☐ False

4. Vocal vibrato is a subtle change in the volume of a note: ☐ True ☐ False

5. Vocal vibrato is written with a wavy line over the noteheads: ☐ True ☐ False

- -

6. Describe what is meant by the term 'vocal range':

   Your answer: ....

   ....

7. Name the two main male vocal ranges:

   Your answer: ....

   ....

BAND ANALYSIS

SUMMARY	
SECTION *(Current section highlighted)*	MARKS
Music Notation	20 [20%]
Popular Music Harmony	25 [25%]
Band Knowledge	25 [25%]
> **Band Analysis**	**30 [30%]**

The *Band Analysis* section of Rockschool Theory Examinations covers the following:

- 4.1   Identify general music features
- 4.2   Accurately complete a score
- 4.3   Identify instrument-specific techniques and stylistic traits
- 5.1   Identify appropriate scales for improvisation

You will be presented with a variety of exercises to hone your understanding and skills in these areas within the content specified for this grade.

Content Overview
An overview of the syllabus content covered at this grade can be found at the back of this book. As this is a cumulative syllabus, you can download overviews for all grades from the Rockschool website at *www.rockschool.co.uk*.

Section 4 | Band Analysis

Band Analysis | Example 1

The following 14 questions relate to the eight-bar score below. Note that there are blank areas which will be filled in as part of the tasks below:

[3]

Section 4 | Band Analysis

1. What key is this piece in?

   Your answer: ....

2. Add chords to beat 1 of the first four bars of the score, basing your analysis on the piano part in each bar.

3. The use of which pedal is required in bars 5 & 6 of the piano part?

   Your answer: ....

4. Which bar contains the chord II m^7 in the first inversion?

   Your answer: ....

5. Add pull-offs to the first two 16th notes in bars 1 & 2 of the guitar part.

6. Which term best describes the melody of the vocal part in bars 1 to 3? *(Tick one box)*

   ☐ Chromatic

   ☐ Scalic

   ☐ Triadic

   ☐ Intervallic

7. In bars 1 to 4 of the drum part, add notation to show that the hi-hat should be played open on beat 1, then closed on the following beat.

8. Add notation to show that the bass guitar should be palm-muted throughout bars 5 & 6.

9. In which part, and in which bar, is there a quarter-note triplet?

   Your answer: ....

10. Add a fermata to all instruments in the final bar that are playing whole-notes.

11. What do you understand by the term ad. lib.?

Your answer: ....

12. Name three musical devices that help to give this piece its character:

Musical device 1: ....

Instrument: ....

Location: ....

Musical device 2: ....

Instrument: ....

Location: ....

Musical device 3: ....

Instrument: ....

Location: ....

Musical device 4: ....

Instrument: ....

Location: ....

13. Using your answers to question 12, along with your knowledge of how these elements typically relate to musical styles, name the style that you think best describes the piece:

Your answer: ....

14. Complete the guitar part by writing out a suitable cont. sim. part in bars 3 and 4, ending the passage with a fill.

Band Analysis | Example 2

The following 12 questions relate to the eight-bar score below. Note that there are blank areas which will be filled in as part of the tasks below:

Section 4 | Band Analysis

1. What key is this piece in?

   Your answer: ....

2. Add symbols to the score to show that it should be swung.

3. Add chords to beat 1 of the first two bars of the score, basing your analysis on the piano and bass-guitar part in each bar.

4. Name the two articulations found in the vocal part:

   Articulation 1 (bar 1): ....

   Articulation 2 (bar 3): ....

5. Name the two articulations found in bar 5 of the guitar part, and explain the difference between them:

   Your answer: ....

   ....

   ....

6. Name the scale used in the guitar part from the first beat of bar 7 to the first beat of bar 8:

   Your answer: ....

7. Add a drum part to complement the guitar and bass parts in bar 8.

8. Identify the articulation over the final notes in the guitar and bass-guitar parts, and briefly explain how this should affect the performances:

   Your answer: ....

   ....

   ....

9. Which of the following instruments play grace notes at some point in the score? *(Tick one or more boxes)*

   ☐ Vocals   ☐ Piano   ☐ Guitar   ☐ Bass guitar   ☐ Drums

10. Name four musical devices that help to give this piece its character:

Musical device 1: ....

Instrument: ....

Location: ....

Musical device 2: ....

Instrument: ....

Location: ....

Musical device 3: ....

Instrument: ....

Location: ....

Musical device 4: ....

Instrument: ....

Location: ....

11. Using your answers to question 10, along with your knowledge of how these elements typically relate to musical styles, name the style that you think best describes the piece:

Your answer: ....

12. Complete the bass-guitar part by writing out a suitable cont. sim. part in bars 3 and 4.

SAMPLE PAPER

The following pages contain examples of the types of questions you will find in a Grade 5 exam paper. They give an indication of the content, format, layout and level at this grade.

You will see the exam paper has been split into the same four sections that have been presented earlier in this workbook:

- Music Notation
- Popular Music Harmony
- Band Knowledge
- Band Analysis

Content Overview

- **Marking:**
  - The exam is marked out of a total of 100, and the total available marks for each section are clearly stated at the start of each section. There is also a blank markbox where your total examination score can be noted.
  - The total marks available for each question are displayed on the right, and include a space for your teacher to mark your answers.

- **General advice:**
  - If a question requires a written answer, don't feel compelled to use every line. Answering the question correctly is much more important than using all the available space.
  - Aim to answer all the questions set. If you get stuck on one particular question, move on and come back to it later.

- **Neatness:**
  - Your answers should be neat, accurate and legible as marks cannot be given if your response is ambiguous.
  - Avoid unnecessary corrections by thinking your responses through before committing them to paper.
  - Use a pencil that is sharp enough to write precisely, but soft enough to rub out and make corrections.
  - To avoid confusion, tick boxes (checkboxes) should be marked with a clear tick symbol rather than a cross. Please note that some answers require more than one box to be ticked, so read the questions carefully.

Please visit *www.rockschool.co.uk* for detailed information on all Rockschool examinations, including syllabus guides, marking schemes and examination entry information.

Grade 5 | Sample Paper

Total marks for this section: 20

Mark:

Q 1.01 | Rewrite this phrase to fit the same number of bars in the new time signature, adjusting the rhythmic values as necessary:

5

Q 1.02 | Rewrite this phrase to fit the same number of bars in the new time signature, adjusting the rhythmic values as necessary:

5

Q 1.03 | Copy the notes from the stave on the left to the stave on the right, one octave higher. Use accidentals instead of a key signature:

5

The following five tasks require you to add notation to the four-bar musical extract below:

Q 1.04 | Indicate that the extract starts pianissimo. `1`

Q 1.05 | Add a symbol to show that the music gradually increases in volume throughout bars 1 & 2. `1`

Q 1.06 | In bar 3, place an accent on the first beat of the bar. `1`

Q 1.07 | Circle the highest note of the extract. `1`

Q 1.08 | Indicate that the final three notes of bar 2 should be played legato. `1`

Section 2 | Popular Music Harmony

Total marks for this section: 25

Mark:

Q 2.01 | Identify the following two melodic intervals and write your answers on the lines below each example:

2

....

Q 2.02 | Add a note to each of the following notes to create the requested harmonic interval:

3

major 3rd below   minor 7th below   perfect 4th above

Q 2.03 | Name the scale used by the following riff:

2

Your answer: ....

Q 2.04 | Add the missing accidentals to the scale below:

2

F harmonic minor

Q 2.05 | Correct this D♭ major scale by adding the missing accidental:

1

D♭   E♭   F   G   A♭   B♭   C   D♭

Q 2.06 | Write the chord names and their inversions below the following chords:

[4]

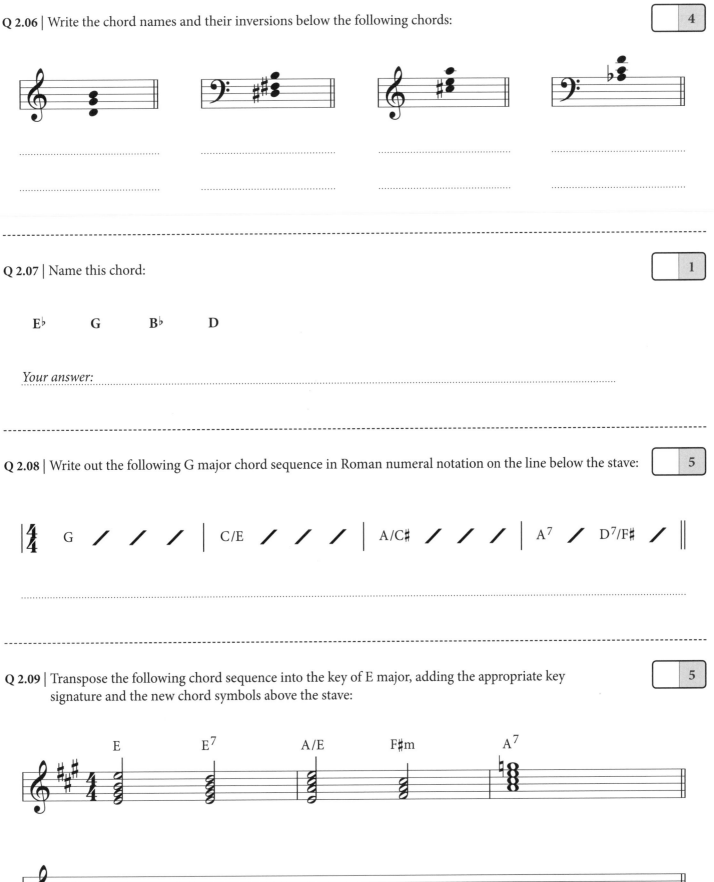

....

....

Q 2.07 | Name this chord:

[1]

E♭   **G**   **B♭**   **D**

Your answer: ....

Q 2.08 | Write out the following G major chord sequence in Roman numeral notation on the line below the stave:

[5]

$\frac{4}{4}$ G / / / | C/E / / / | A/C♯ / / / | A^7 / D^7/F♯ / ‖

....

Q 2.09 | Transpose the following chord sequence into the key of E major, adding the appropriate key signature and the new chord symbols above the stave:

[5]

Section 3 | Band Knowledge | Part 1 – Identification

Total marks for this section:	25

Mark:	

Q 3.01 | Which drum can be operated by a pair of foot pedals, and which style of music might you hear this in? | 2 |

Your answer: ....

Q 3.02 | Which part of the drum kit uses a clutch? | 1 |

Your answer: ....

Q 3.03 | What tool is used to change the tension and pitch of a drum head? | 1 |

Your answer: ....

The following four questions require you to identify parts of the guitar as labelled in the image on the right:

Q 3.04 | Which letter points to the volume control? | 1 |

Your answer: ....

Q 3.05 | Which letter points to the pickup selector? | 1 |

Your answer: ....

Q 3.06 | Which letter points to the pickups?

| 1 |

Your answer: ....

Q 3.07 | Which letter points to the jack socket?

| 1 |

Your answer: ....

Q 3.08 | Which EQ setting makes the sound fuller and warmer?

| 1 |

Your answer: ....

Q 3.09 | Which EQ setting makes the sound light and sparkly?

| 1 |

Your answer: ....

Q 3.10 | Which pedal lifts the dampers off the strings of an acoustic piano, allowing the sound to ring out?

| 1 |

Your answer: ....

Q 3.11 | Give two examples of basic controls typically found on a PA:

| 2 |

1. ....

2. ....

Section 3 | Band Knowledge | Part 2 – Notation & Techniques

The following three questions refer to the one-bar extract of drum notation below:

Each beat of the bar uses a different snare-drum technique. Identify the technique used for the following beats:

Q 3.12 | Beat 2:   [ ] 1

Your answer: ....

Q 3.13 | Beat 3:   [ ] 1

Your answer: ....

Q 3.14 | Beat 4:   [ ] 1

Your answer: ....

The following two questions relate to the two-bar extract of guitar notation below:

Q 3.15 | What does the NH mean in bar 1?   [ ] 1

Your answer: ....

Q 3.16 | Explain how a guitarist would play the notes labelled with NH: [ ] 2

Your answer: ....

The following three tasks require you to add notation to the two-bar extract of piano notation below:

Q 3.17 | Add a diminuendo symbol in the second bar, from beat 3 to beat 4. `1`

Q 3.18 | Add appropriate pedal indications, lifting the pedal at the end of each bar. `1`

Q 3.19 | Add a staccato to the lowest-pitched note in the bass part. `1`

Q 3.20 | What does the letter 'A' stand for in SATB? `1`

Your answer:

Q 3.21 | Explain what the term 'vocal range' means: `1`

Your answer:

Q 3.22 | Which of the following is a description of vocal vibrato? *(Tick one box)* `1`

☐ A subtle oscillation in the pitch of a note.

☐ A rapid change in the volume of the note.

☐ A rapid fluctuation between two different vowel sounds.

Grade 5 | Sample Paper

Section 4 | Band Analysis

Mark:

The following 11 questions relate to the eight-bar score below. Note that there are blank areas that are to be filled in as part of the tasks that follow:

[3]

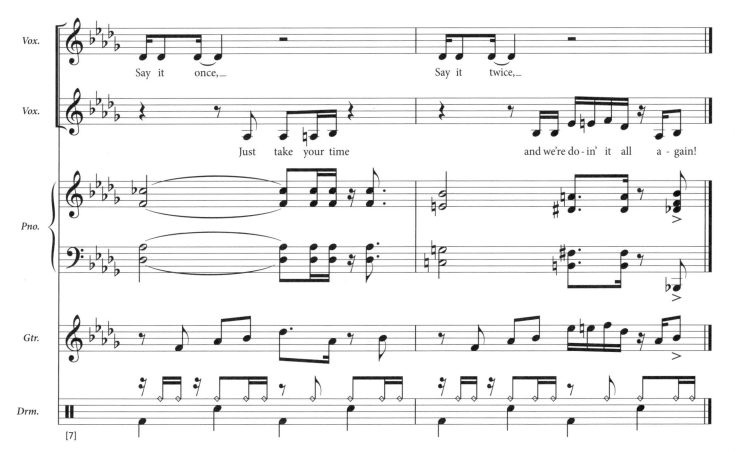

Q 4.01 | Name the key used in this piece:

1

Your answer: ....

Q 4.02 | Add a chord symbol above beat 1 of bar 1 based on what you see in the piano part.

1

Q 4.03 | Add a chord symbol over the following beats, based on what you see in the piano part:

Bar 1, beat 1 — 1

Bar 3, beat 1 — 1

Bar 3, beat 3 — 1

Q 4.04 | Name a single symbol that you could place at the start of the score to indicate that an instrument should play loudly, then immediately quietly:

1

Your answer: ....

Q 4.05 | Which drum voice is played in the upper part (with stems up) of the drums throughout? *(Tick one box)*

1

☐ Ride   ☐ Open hi-hat   ☐ Ride bell   ☐ Ghost snare   ☐ Rim shot

Q 4.06 | Name the harmonic interval (e.g. perfect 4th) formed between the vocal parts on beat 2 of bar 1:

1

Your answer: ....

Q 4.07 | Name three musical devices that help to give this piece its character:

| 6 |

Musical device 1: ....

Instrument: ....

Location: ....

Musical device 2: ....

Instrument: ....

Location: ....

Musical device 3: ....

Instrument: ....

Location: ....

Q 4.08 | Using your answers to question 4.07, along with your knowledge of how these elements typically relate to musical styles, name the style that you think best describes the piece:

| 2 |

Your answer: ....

Q 4.09 | Name two things that the guitarist could do to the part or to their sound to add more of a metal edge to the piece:

| 2 |

1. ....

2. ....

Q 4.10 | Name two scales that would be a good choice to use for improvising over the first two bars of the piece:

| 4 |

Your answer: ....

Q 4.11 | Complete the drum part by writing out a suitable cont. sim. part in bars 5 & 6. Include a two-beat fill where appropriate.

| 8 |

Syllabus Content Overview | Grade 5

Important: This table represents content that is new at this grade. The content of Rockschool Theory Examinations is cumulative, so Grades 1 to 8 include all content from previous grades in the syllabus. A full version of this table is available online at *www.rockschool.co.uk*, and includes details of content at every grade.

Section	Content	Details
1: Music Notation (20%)	1.1: Pitch	pitch range: 15ma, 15mb symbols
	1.2: Note length/rhythm	half-note triplet
	1.3: Dynamics, articulations, phrasing	dynamics: *fp*, *sfp*
2: Popular Music Harmony (25%)	2.1: Scales and related intervals	major scales: B, D♭
		natural minor scales: B♭m, G♯m
		harmonic minor scale formula
		harmonic minor scales: Am, Em, Bm, F♯m, C♯m, G♯m, Dm, Gm, Cm, Fm, B♭m
		harmonic and melodic intervals: minor 6th, minor 7th
	2.2: Chords	major chords: B, D♭
		major arpeggios: B, D♭
		minor chords: G♯m, B♭m
		minor arpeggios: G♯m, B♭m
		chord inversions: 1st, 2nd inversions
		transposition of chord symbols
3: Band Knowledge (25%)	3.1: Identify instrument parts and function	drums: double bass-drum pedal, hi-hat clutch
		guitar and bass guitar: jack socket, amp input
		keys: EQ, tone
		vocals: microphone, PA
	3.2: Identify instrument-specific notation	drum notation: rim shots, drag
		guitar and bass-guitar notation: natural harmonics (NH), pinched harmonics (PH), instrument pitch ranges
		keys notation: glissando, instrument range
		vocal notation: vibrato, SATB vocal ranges
	3.3: Identify instrumental techniques	as listed above in 3.2
4: Band Analysis (30%)	4.1: Identify general music features listed	identify and show understanding of the applied musical elements listed within the first three sections (above) within the context of a score
		instrument range: drum kit, guitar, bass guitar, keyboard, vocals
		number of parts: 5
		piece length: 8 bars
	4.2: Accurately complete a score	be able to construct a 2 bar cont. sim. part for any of the instruments listed within the 5 part score, to include a fill
	4.3: Identify instrument-specific techniques and stylistic traits	as listed within part 3 (above)
		identify musical and stylistic devices used within the score (pop, blues, rock, metal, funk)
	5.1: Identify appropriate scales for improvisation	identify appropriate scale for improvising over a chord sequence within the score: scales as listed within part 2

rockschool ®

ENTER ONLINE

Ready to take your Rockschool Theory Exam?

Now it's easier than ever...

1 GO TO WWW.ROCKSCHOOL.CO.UK/ENTER-ONLINE

2 CREATE AN ACCOUNT

3 SELECT YOUR EXAM CENTRE AND DATE

4 CHOOSE YOUR GRADE

...and you're ready to go.

Book your exam today – go to **www.rockschool.co.uk/enter-online**, or email **info@rockschool.co.uk** for more information.